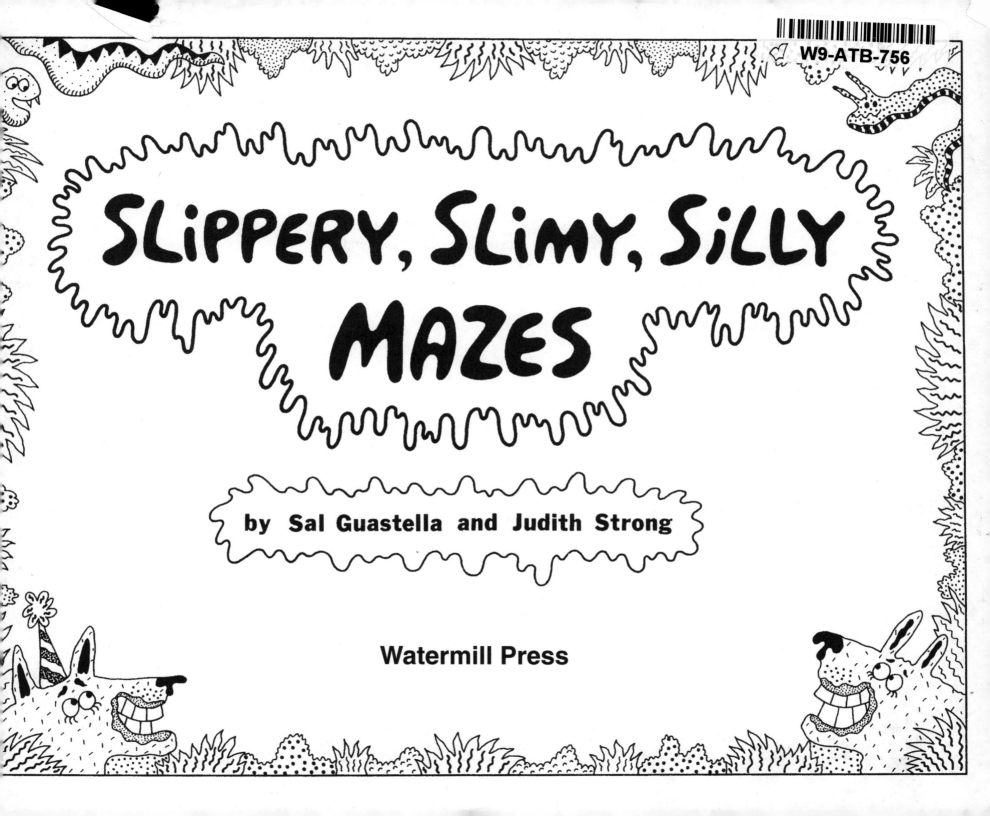

SLiPPERY, SLiMY, SiLLY MAZES

by Sal Guastella and Judith Strong

Watermill Press

We dedicate this book to our good friends
Don Bagwell and Kelly Swope

Published by Watermill Press.
Copyright © 1994 by Sal Guastella and Judith Strong.
Printed in the United States of America.
10 9 8 7 6 5 4 3 2 1

WELCOME!

Mazes that are slippery, slimy
Make your eyes red and shiny.
We've invented these to do, so
See if you can muddle through
The twisting, turning, learning mazes
Waiting on these fun-filled pages!

"BUGS in the BRAIN"

Baffled Dr. Bartholomew discovered bugs in the brain. Grab each gooey grub and drop them in the buggy bowl.

DID YOU KNOW...?

Some ancient people believed that headaches were caused by demons trapped inside the head.

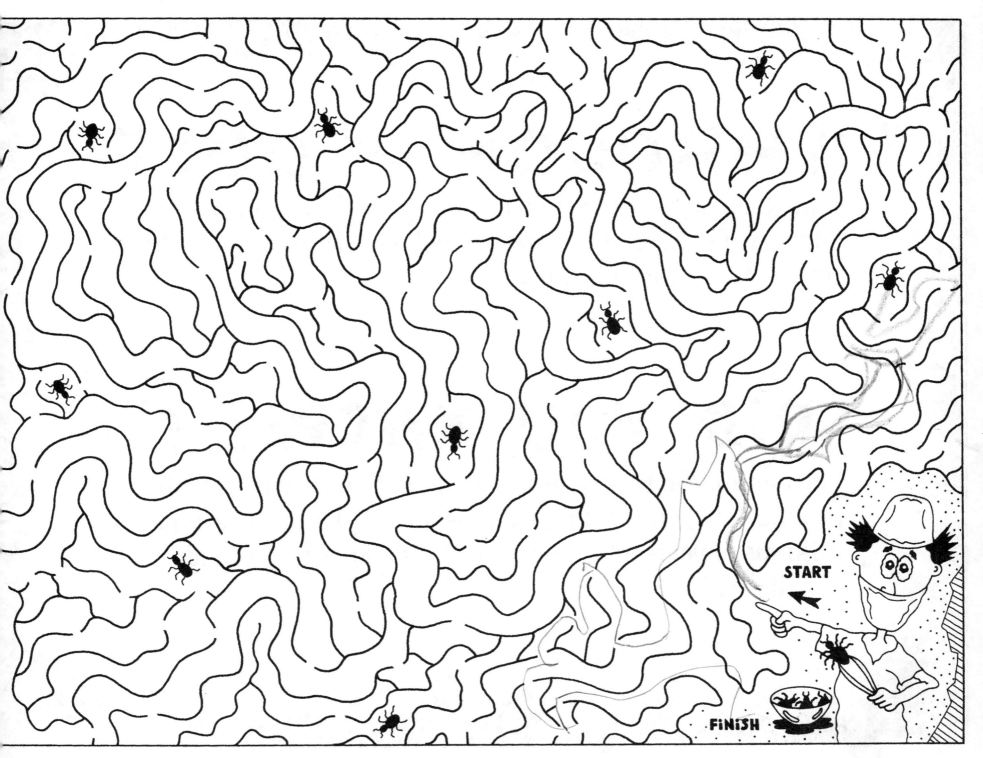

START

FINISH

"THROUGH THE OOZE"

Can Ken and Karen clear a clean course through the slippery oil slick? A viscous veil will cover them unless they find a way to shut the valve!

DID YOU KNOW...?

Petroleum, the source of gasoline, fuel oil, and many other products, began forming from decaying plants and animals millions of years ago. That's why it's sometimes called "fossil fuel."

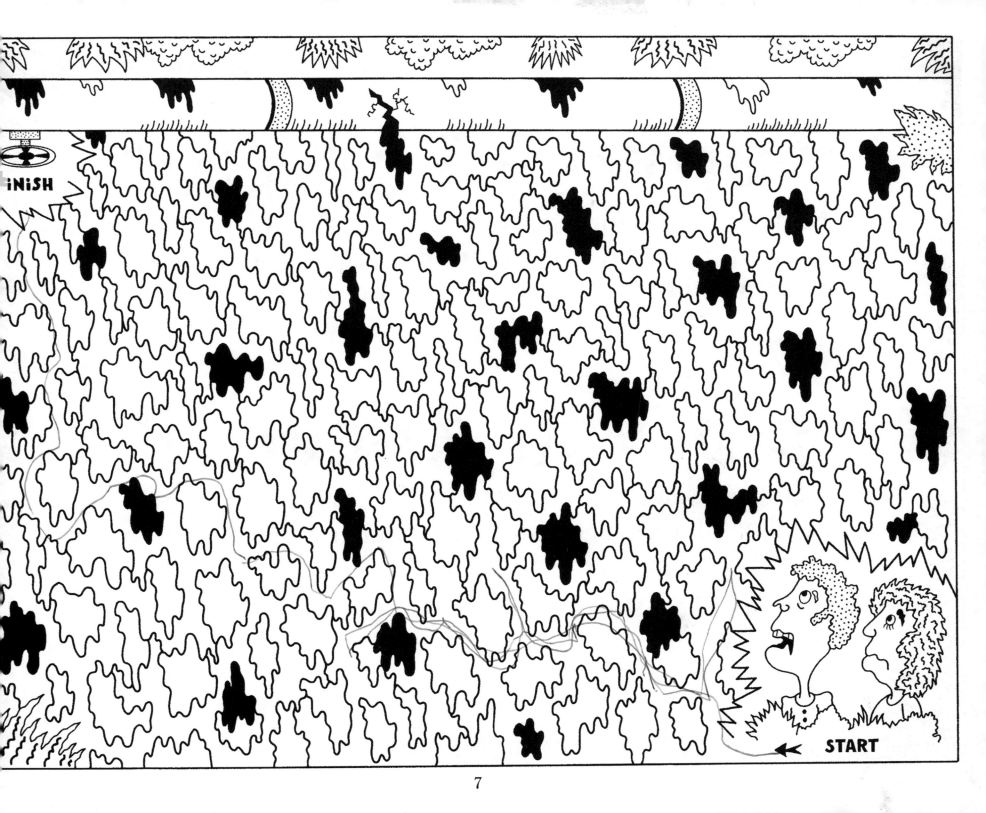

FINISH

START

7

"DOWN THE DRAIN"

Foolish Freddy dropped his mother's dazzling diamond ring down the drain. Recovering the ring requires some tight twists and turns. If you're ready, please help Freddy!

DID YOU KNOW...?

Diamond engagement rings were first popular in Europe hundreds of years ago. One of the youngest brides-to-be to wear such a ring was two-year-old Princess Mary of England upon her engagement to the infant Prince of France in the year 1518!

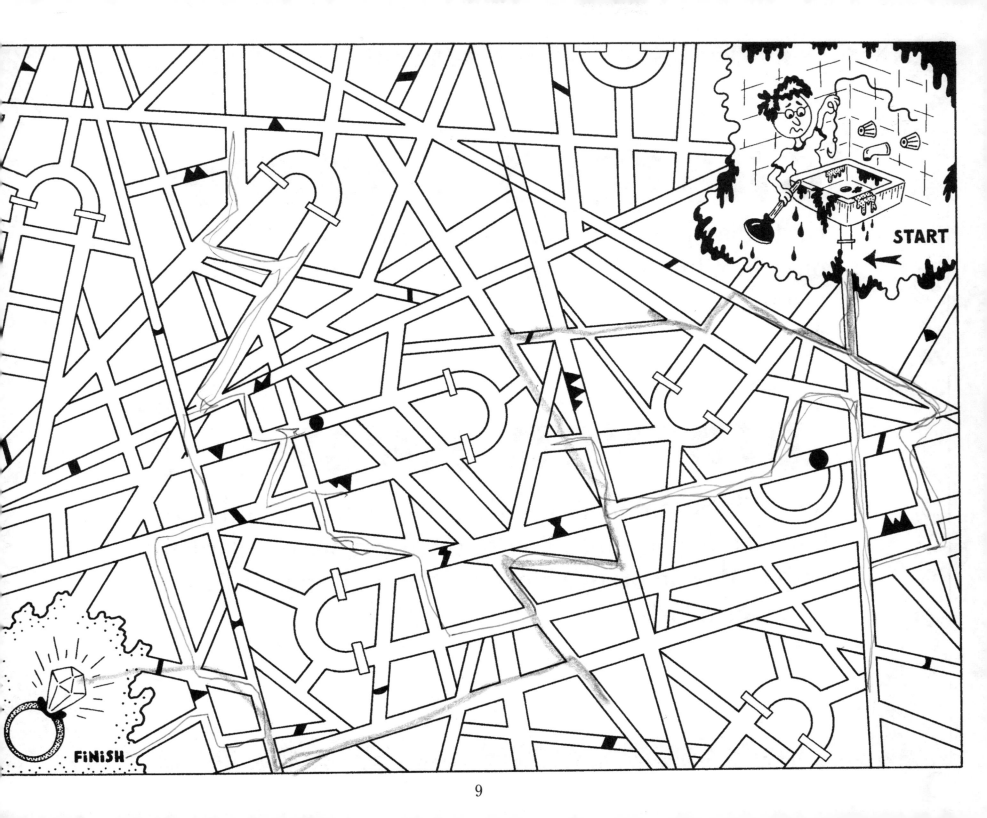

START

FINISH

"GILBERT'S GARBAGE"

Gertrude's grandson, Gilbert, is stuck in a rancid refuse pile. Plot his perfect path to the delightful daisies in the distance.

DID YOU KNOW...?

Sometimes combinations of smells cancel each other out. For example, if you combined the fragrance of a gardenia with that of an orange blossom, the resulting mixture would be odorless!

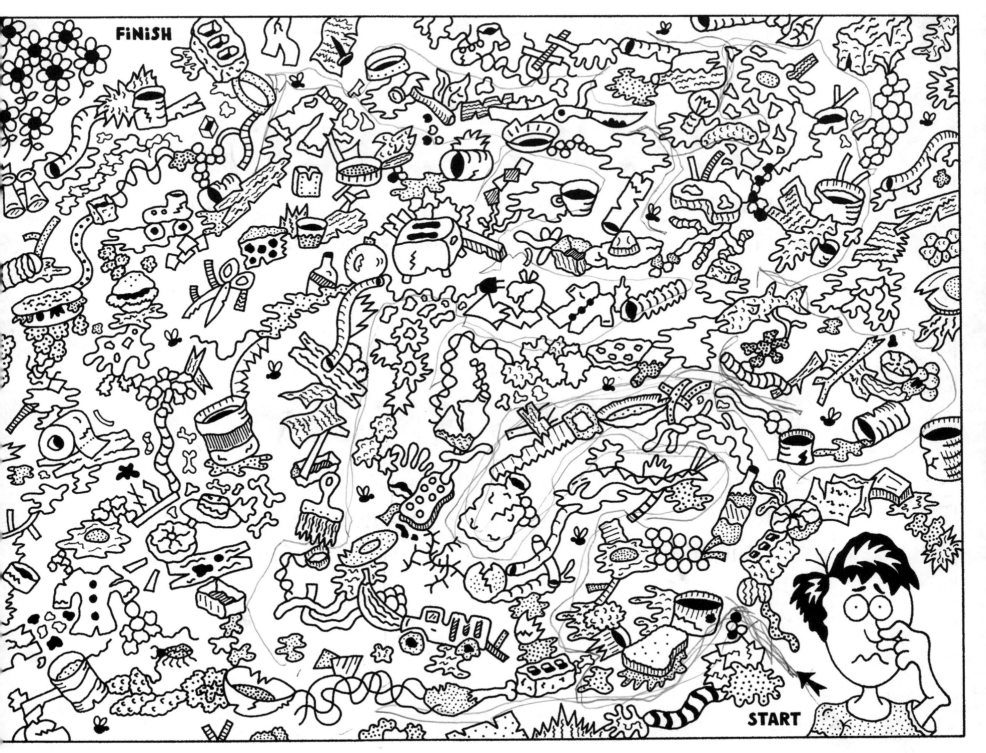

FINISH

START

11

"STICKY STUFF"

Messy, mucky maple syrup is spilling all over. Don't get glued by the gunk. Swiftly seal the sweet treat!

DID YOU KNOW...?

Maple syrup is made from maple sugar, which is made from the sap of maple trees. It takes 35-45 gallons (132-170 l) of maple sap to make just one gallon (3.79 l) of maple syrup!

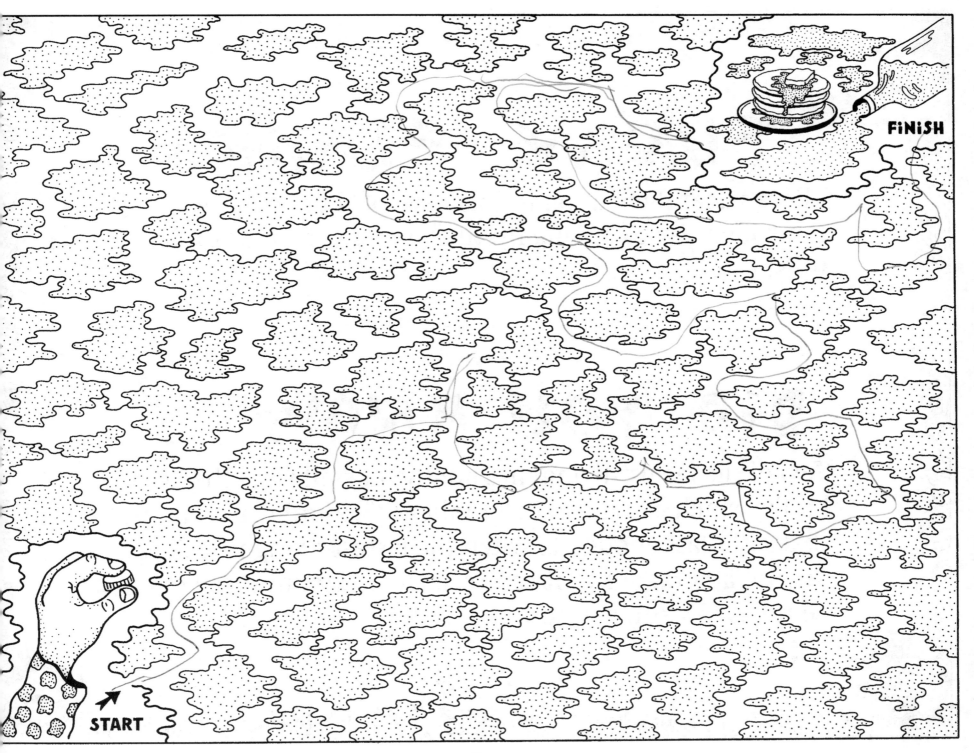

START

FINISH

"FUNKY FLAKES"

There's a fat fly floating in this bowl of "Funky Flakes." Find your way to the big fly, flick it away, then flit to the finish!

DID YOU KNOW...?

Two of the fastest-flying flies are the horsefly and the deer botfly, which can fly up to 24 miles (38.6 km) per hour. But that's not fast enough to catch the fastest-flying insect, the Australian dragonfly. It can reach a maximum speed of 36 miles (58 km) per hour!

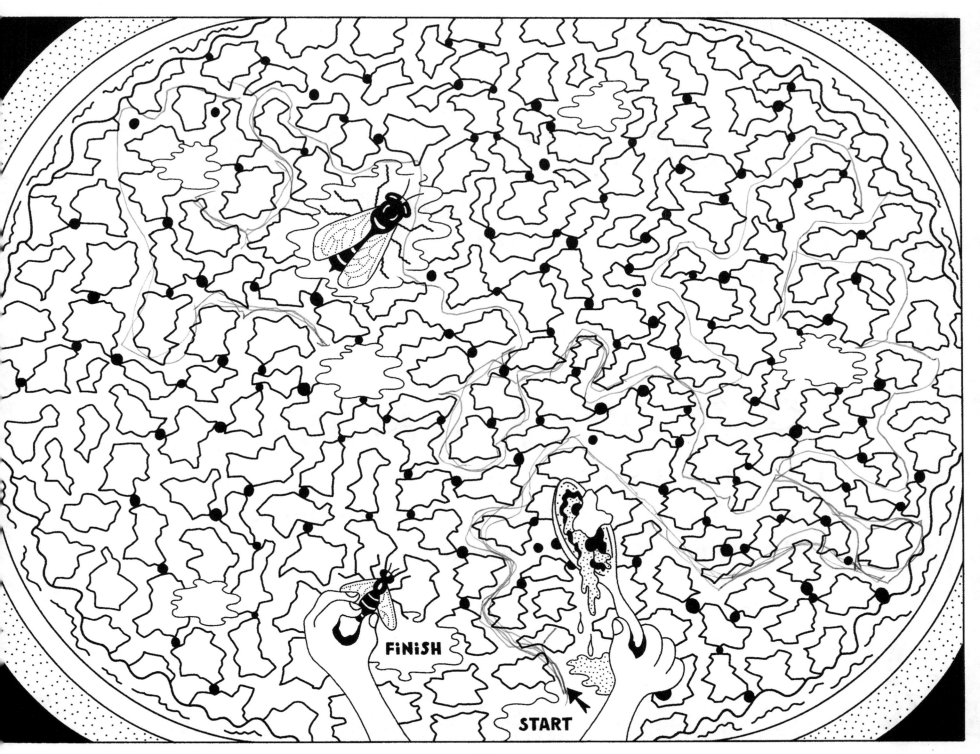

FINISH

START

"MUMMY DEAREST"

In the dark, dank depths of a Pharaoh's pyramid, archaeologists Anna and Arnie bumped into bundles of bandages. Help them unravel the wrappings to unveil the moldy mummy.

DID YOU KNOW...?

Ancient Egyptian priests sometimes dined with mummies! During banquets, a large mummy was sometimes brought to the table to remind the guests how precious life is.

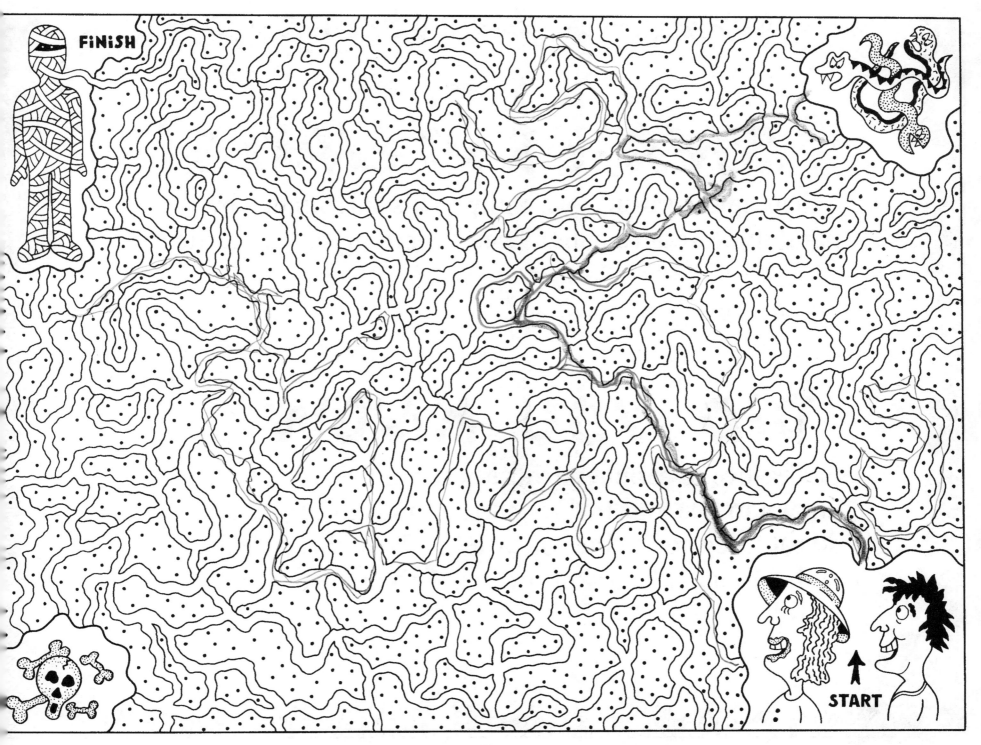

FINISH

START

17

"SNAILS AND NAILS"

Scoop up the seven slow, slimy snails surrounded by naughty Norman's nails. Then take them to the plastic pail.

DID YOU KNOW...?

Snails love to eat plants, but these animals have been known to live four to five years without eating! When snails do eat, they don't chew like we do. They shred their food with a tonguelike organ covered with hundreds of tiny teeth!

START

FINISH

19

"SEEING EYE TO EYE"

Vinny's vision is very poor, posing a problem for this pitiful pup. Spotting spectacles in the distance, he has to discover a path through these icky eyes.

DID YOU KNOW...?

Five thousand years ago the Chinese soothed tired eyes with the world's first eye drops, which they made from an extract of the mahuang plant. Eye drops today contain the same ingredient!

START

FINISH

21

"LOUNGING LARRY"

Larry the lounging lizard is out of luck. There is turbulence on the TV. Please locate the lost channel changer in the jumbled jungle of vines and take it back to this lazy lizard.

DiD YOU KNOW...?

There are more than 3,000 species of lizards in the world, more than any other living reptile. They range from a 2" (5 cm)-long gecko found in the British Virgin Islands to the incredible 15' 7" (4.75 m)-long Salvadori monitor of Papua, New Guinea.

FINISH

START

"HOUSE WORMING"

Wanda wishes the wiggly worms weren't blocking the way to her front door. Please help her get home!

DID YOU KNOW...?

Earthworms come in all sizes. The tiniest is smaller than a flea. The longest earthworm, found in South Africa in the 1930's, measured an incredible 22' (6.71 m) long!

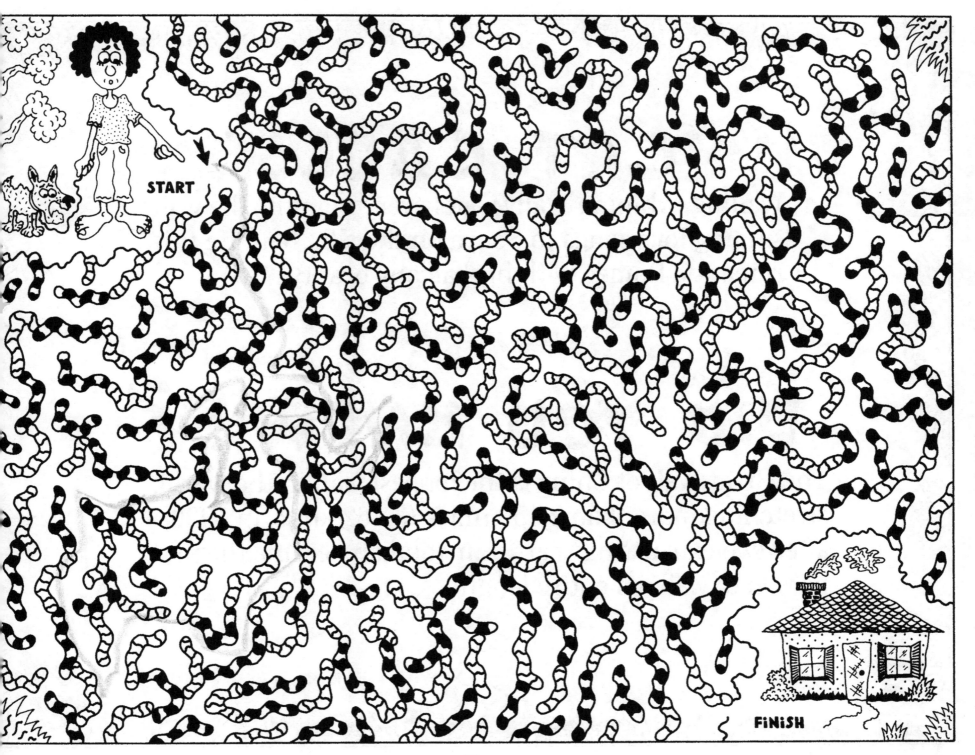

START

FINISH

25

"CAT CALLS"

Wailing, whining Wally waits every night by the wall, singing love songs to Sonya on the sill. Reunite this romantic Romeo with his balcony beauty.

DID YOU KNOW...?

The Great Wall of China is the longest wall in the world, stretching more than 2,150 miles (3,462 km)! In 1990, after two exhausting years, Lin Youdian became the first person to walk its entire length.

FINISH

START ➤➤

27

"BRUCE'S BROW"

Bothersome bugs are beginning to swim in the sweat on Bruce's brow. Take the tick past the perspiration flowing from his face.

DiD YOU KNOW...?

Human sweat is clear and colorless, but the sweat of the African hippopotamus is blood-red!

START

FINISH

29

"SEEING STARS"

Standar is stuck on solid ground while his spacecraft spins in outer space. Target a trajectory through the stars to take this anxious alien back to his ship.

DID YOU KNOW...?

The sun is just one of an estimated 200 billion-billion stars in the universe. It takes sunlight only 8 minutes, 20 seconds to reach Earth. But light from our next nearest star, Proxima Centauri, takes 4 years, 15 ½ weeks to reach us!

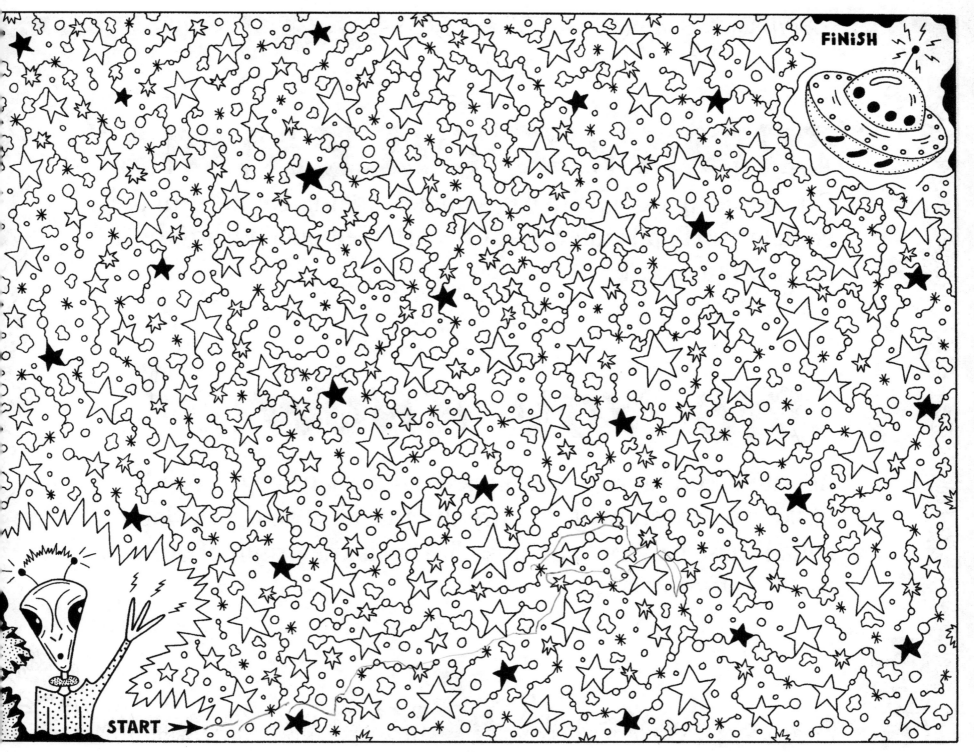

FINISH

START ➤

"DINKY'S DILEMMA"

Dudley's dopey dog Dinky has done it again! He's lost in the cemetery. Help Dudley pluck his petrified pooch from the ghostly graveyard.

DID YOU KNOW...?

About 6,000 years ago the ancient Sumerians began using baskets of woven twigs to bury their dead. The Greeks later called these baskets "kophinos." This is the origin of our word "coffin."

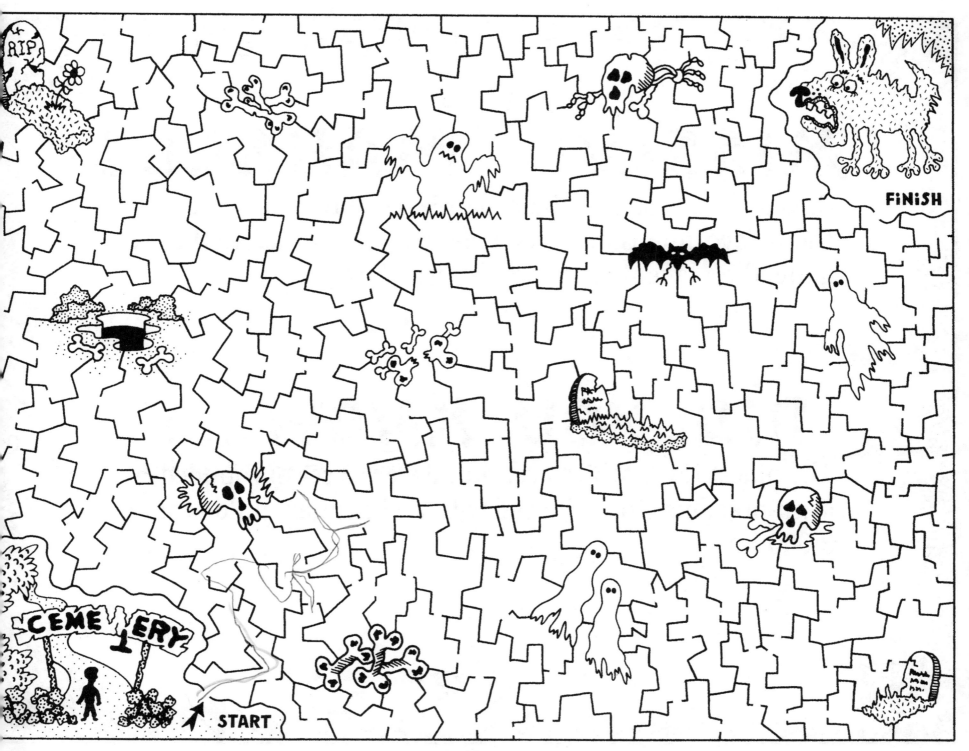

RIP

FINISH

CEMETERY

START

"MISSING MARBLES"

Sam and Sally spilled their marbles, and this frog finds them flavorful! Gather each gleaming globe before they're gone, then take them to the famished frog.

DID YOU KNOW...?

The oldest toy marbles ever found were a set of rounded semi-precious stones buried with an Egyptian child around 3,000 B.C.

FINISH

START

"I. C. BONES"

The succulent scent of bones is bugging Boomey and Barney. Which garbage can contains these canines' favorite treat?

DID YOU KNOW...?

In 11th-century Norway, the people chose a dog to be their king! King "Suening-Saur," a dog, reigned for three years and signed all official documents with his paw print!

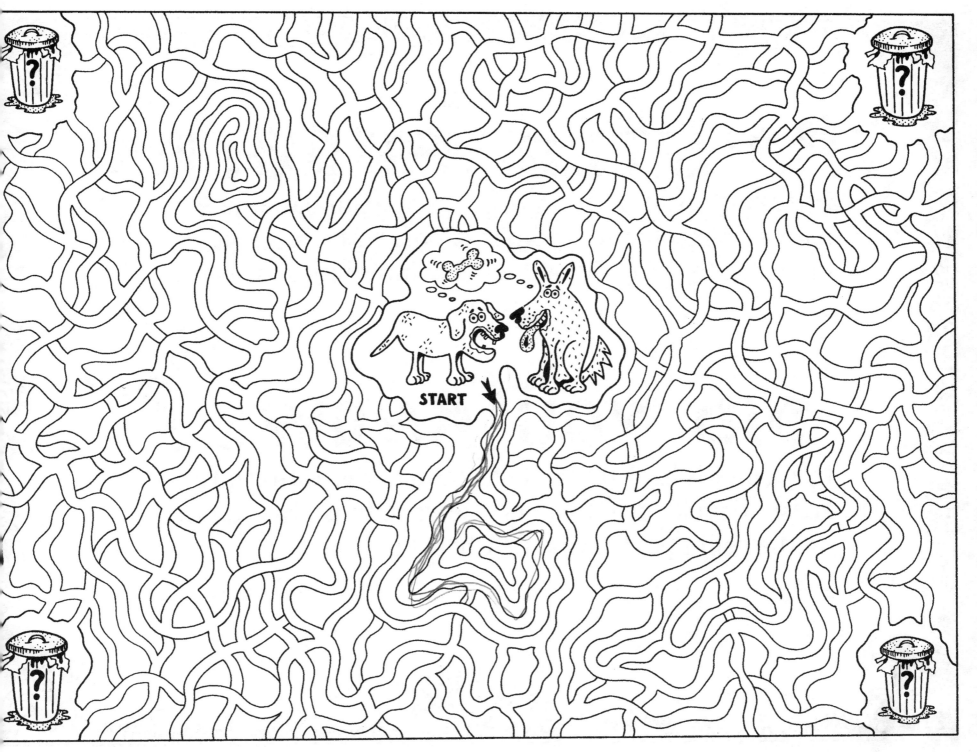

START

"PAINTED PROBLEM"

Streaking strokes of purple pigment, Paul has almost painted himself into a corner. Consider the correct direction to the door before the painter plugs his path.

DID YOU KNOW...?

Lying on his back on top of a scaffold, the 16th-century artist Michelangelo took four years to finish his painting on the ceiling of the Sistine Chapel in Rome.

FINISH

START

"SNAKE PIT"

Vicious, venomous vipers are keeping these kids from finding the path out of the pit. Follow the flashlight's beam, but avoid the slithering serpents!

DID YOU KNOW...?

Cobras can't hear the sound of a snake-charmer's flute. That's because snakes are nearly deaf! They "dance" by following the movement and vibration of the flute.

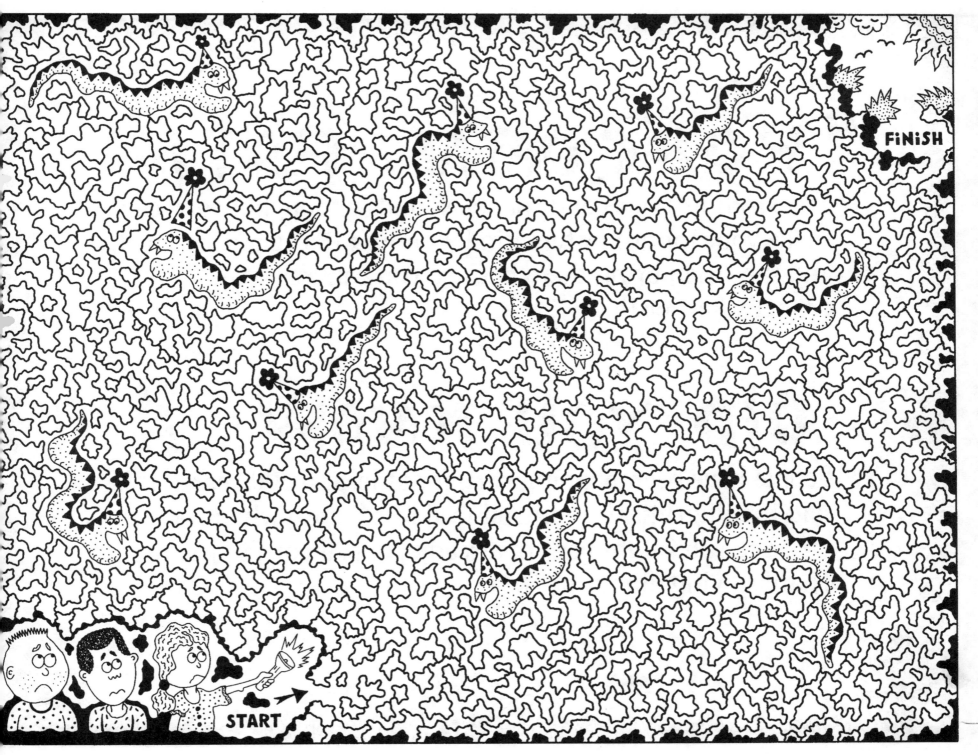

FINISH

START

41

"POPCORN PATH"

The sizzling smells and snappy sounds of popping corn can make your mouth water. Find your way to the butter, bowl, and salt, then bring them back so you can enjoy the crunchy kernels!

DID YOU KNOW...?

People have been popping corn for at least 5,000 years. It is said the Pilgrims were introduced to popcorn when Native Americans brought bags of already-popped corn to the first Thanksgiving dinner in 1621.

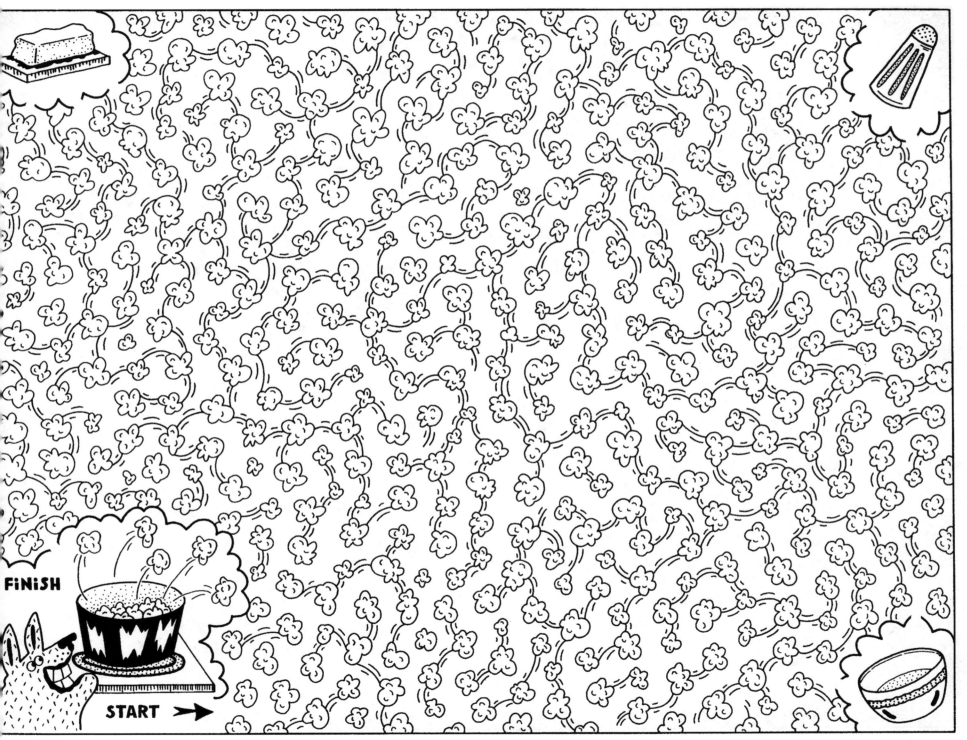

FINISH

START ➤

ANSWERS
Here are our solutions, but you might find different ones!

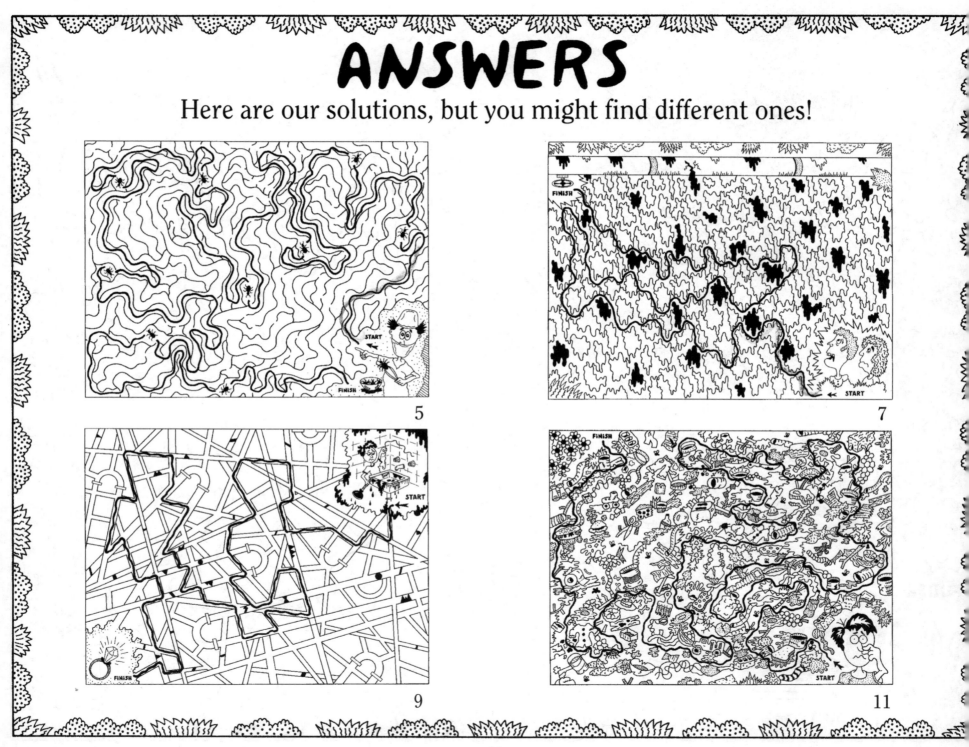

5

7

9

11